FOURTH CONCERTO

IN D MINOR

FOR

PIANO & ORCHESTRA

OP. 70

BY

ANTON RUBINSTEIN

3079

SUGGESTIONS FOR USING THIS MMO EDITION

WE HAVE TRIED to create a product that will provide you an easy way to learn and perform a concerto with a full orchestra in the comfort of your own home. Because it involves a fixed orchestral performance, there is an inherent lack of flexibility in tempo and cadenza length. The following MMO features and techniques will reduce these inflexibilities and help you maximize the effectiveness of the MMO practice and performance system:

Where the soloist begins a movement *solo*, we have provided an introductory measure with subtle taps inserted at the actual tempo before the soloist's entrance.

Chapter stops on your CD are conveniently located throughout the piece at the beginnings of practice sections, and are cross-referenced in the score. This should help you quickly find a desired place in the music as you learn the piece.

Chapter stops have also been placed at orchestra entrances (after cadenzas, for example) so that, with the help of a second person, it is possible to perform a seamless version of the concerto alongside your MMO CD accompaniment. While we have allotted what is generally considered an average amount of time for a cadenza, each performer will have a different interpretation and observe individual tempi. Your personal rendition may preclude a perfect "fit" within the space provided. Therefore, by having a second person press the pause ❚❚ button on your CD player after the start of each cadenza, followed by the next track ▶▶❚ button, your CD will be cued to the orchestra's re-entry. When you as soloist are at the end of the cadenza or other solo passage, the second person can press the play ▶ (or pause ❚❚ button) on the CD remote to allow a synchronized orchestra re-entry.

Regarding tempi: we have observed generally accepted tempi, but some may wish to perform at a different tempo, or to slow down or speed up the accompaniment for practice purposes. You can purchase from MMO (or from other audio and electronics dealers) specialized CD players which allow variable speed while maintaining proper pitch. This is an indispensable tool for the serious musician and you may wish to look into purchasing this useful piece of equipment for full enjoyment of all your MMO editions.

We want to provide you with the most useful practice and performance accompaniments possible. If you have any suggestions for improving the MMO system, please feel free to contact us. You can reach us by e-mail at info@musicminusone.com.

MUSIC MINUS ONE

3079

ANTON RUBINSTEIN

FOURTH
CONCERTO
IN D MINOR

FOR

PIANO & ORCHESTRA
OP. 70

Anton Rubinstein's Piano concerto No. 4 in D minor, op. 70

Anton Grigoryevich Rubinstein was born on 28 November (16 November old calendar) 1829 in Vichvatijnetz, a village on the Dniester in southern Russia, which today lies in Moldova. His Jewish family's conversion to Christianity was due undoubtedly to the oppressive attitude towards Jews during the regime of Czar Nicholas I. His mother was a fine musician as well as his first teacher, and it was she who instilled in him a severe sense of discipline in study. She fed her son a diet of Hummel, Hertz, Moscheles, Kalkbrenner, Czerny, Diabelli, and Clementi and this gave the boy a firm groundwork on which to build and astonishing career.

He later studied with a well-known pianist/composer named Alexander Villoing, who was to nurture him through his initial successes on the concert platform as a small boy. Rubinstein gained his first flush of fame at a remarkably early age, in a period when child prodigies were all the rage. Indeed, he was a mere ten years old in 1840 when he played for Chopin and Liszt; it was Liszt who recognized the boy's unique talents and astutely predicted a great career for him. Liszt instructed Villoing to take the boy to Berlin for further study, which he duly did. In turn, several years later, Rubinstein was taken to one of Liszt's recitals and was so affected that he collapsed. Liszt is supposed to have maintained vigil by the youth until he recovered. There was always a fondness between these two men, even though they had their differences, especially in the area of compositional style. No small measure of this, however, can be attributed to the egos which accompanied both of these great artists. Rubinstein was a strongly opinionated man and was often loose with his tongue. While he roundly praised his good friend Liszt's performing, he was dismissive—as were many of his day—of that musical giant's compositional powers. Interestingly the same kind of tone came from Liszt himself, who felt that Rubinstein was enormously talented as a composer but fished too much "in Mendelssohnian waters." And indeed Rubinstein stood in awe of Mendelssohn, who was a bridge between the classical and romantic worlds; and like that master and Johannes Brahms, Rubinstein seemed to have one foot in the classical world of Beethoven and another in the Romantic world of Chopin and Liszt.

Rubinstein professed that while he felt Germans were the most musical of people, the English were the least. Ironically, it was an English audience that, on the night after Rubinstein's death in 1894, rose to their feet as Josef Hofmann played the 'Funeral March' portion of Chopin's B-flat-minor Sonata and bowed their heads in honor of Rubinstein, whose interpretation of that sonata was legendary.

Rubinstein was a man of paradoxes, a fact borne out by his famous statement:

> Russians call me a German, Germans call me a Russian, Jews call me a Christian, Christians a Jew. Pianists call me a composer, composers call me a pianist. The classicists think me a futurist, and the futurists a reactionary. My conclusion is that I am neither fish, flesh nor good red herring—a pitiful individual.

For pianists Anton Rubinstein stands as a god second only to Liszt; his overwhelming presence and his magical ability to make the piano alternately sing and thunder makes him to this day an object of wonder and a model to which future concert-artists aspire. Sadly, Rubinstein died before the advent of the gramophone and we are left to discover his artistry from second-hand accounts, or from recordings of Rubinstein's brilliant student Josef Hofmann, who at least melded some of his master's technique into his own very unique style of playing.

It is the performance aspect of Rubinstein's compositions —most of which fell out of the repertoire during the anti-Romantic mid-20th Century—which has caused much controversy in the present day as his music comes under re-evaluation. Rubinstein's compositions come to life when a performer can capture the spark of his unique and very special performance techniques to create the peaks and valleys, the climaxes and anti-climaxes which are not necessarily visible on the printed page of his compositions. Rubinstein was an intense man and he had a performance style to match, which he may have summed up best when he told Josef Hofmann, upon hearing him play the same phrase twice in a piece in an identical manner, "In fine weather you may play it as you did, but when it rains play it differently."

It is through Hofmann's written recollections of Rubinstein's teaching and playing that we know much of the great lion's technique. Hofmann described Rubinstein's playing thus: "Rubinstein excelled by his sincerity, by his demoniacal, Heaven-storming power of great impassionedness, qualities which with Liszt had passed through the sieve of a superior education and—if you understand how I mean that term—gentlemanly elegance. He was, in the highest meaning of the word, a man of the world; Rubinstein, a world-stormer, with a sovereign disregard for conventionality...."

As far as technique, Hofmann said that "with Rubinstein there was no *ignus fatuus* of mere method. Any method that would lead to fine artistic results—to beautiful and effective performance—was justifiable in his eyes." Indeed, the great master had told his young pupil, "the main object is to make the music sound right, even if you have to play with your nose!" And it is interesting that Rubinstein, who was famous for hitting wrong notes in his concerts—to the utter indifference of his audiences—was such a stickler for accuracy in his teaching. Said Hofmann: "Once I called his attention modestly to this seeming paradox, and he answered: 'When you are as old as I am now you may do as I do—if you can.'"

Perhaps the most revealing statements about Rubinstein's artistry come from the man himself. When asked how he could make such an impression on an audience, he said, "Perhaps it is due partly to the very great volume of sound, but mainly because I have put in a lot of work in order to succeed in making the piano sing." Here, no doubt, is much of the essence of his abilities. He also said that the pedal was the soul of the piano.

The Fourth Concerto was composed in 1864 and was published in 1866; Rubinstein later made revisions for a second and final edition which was published in 1872. The concerto was immensely popular and influential. Immediately becoming a staple of the concerto repertoire, it had enormous influence on Tchaikovsky, whose now-famous B-flat-minor concerto No. 1 was heavily influenced by the work, as there are many parallels to be found between the two concerti.

The disappearance of the Fourth Concerto from concert programs after the Second World War is all the more perplexing because it was so popular for nearly eighty years; every great pianist from Hofmann to Rachmaninov and Horowitz played it to thunderous cheers. It was recorded by many masters of the early and mid-20th Century, and was memorably performed in such prominent Hollywood movies as *The Great Lie* (1941) and *The Other Love* (1947).

Pianist Shura Cherkassky (1911-1995) told David Dubal in *Reflections from the Keyboard* that he had been mightily impressed by Josef Hoffman's playing of the Fourth Concerto and that the piece was one of his own personal favorites. "I love the piece; it's in the spirit of the grand manner...But the concerto is unfortunately not played anymore...it is a loss to the public, which gets needlessly the same thing over and over." Indeed, Cherkassky was intent on performing the piece as late as the 1980s.

Legendary pianist-composer Ignaz Paderewski described the Fourth Concerto as "really overwhelming—impossible to describe....The whole of the first movement is a masterpiece. It is just as if it had been born, like Minerva, from the brain of Jupiter."

Now, at the dawn of the twenty-first century, the piano-world and the public have again begun to rediscover this amazing concerto, as well as many of Rubinstein's other works.

The Fourth Concerto begins with a deepeningly ominous introduction by the orchestra; then the piano bursts forth in a shattering version of the main theme. This thunderous opening gives little hint of the lyrical beauty that will follow soon thereafter; but arrive it does, and the entire movement, filled with massive amounts of solo material for the piano, leaves an indelible impression. The second movement is heart-melting, with its singularly vocal melody, one that does not leave the listener's head easily. It is easy to see how influenced Rubinstein was by opera, and proof of his conviviality with that genre, that he was able to bring out the vocal qualities of the piano with such apparent facility. In the third movement, a turbulent, stormy undercurrent bubbles forth into a torrent. The wild, dance-like, pianistic frenzy that follows is pure Rubinstein; one can almost see him on the concert-platform in a whirl of passionate abandon. The overall effect is thrilling, and it is hard to find anything since that can be as overwhelming.

August Göllerich, Franz Liszt's amanuensis during the last years of his life, recorded some comments Liszt made to his student Alexander Lambert regarding the playing of Rubinstein's Fourth Concerto:

Regarding the first theme (m. 39): "You must play thus, broadly; emphasize the first quarter-note and conceive the theme in a grandiose manner. Not so dancelike; play each quarter-note equally. Then it sounds very authentic—you already know what I want to say!" At that he made the corresponding motion. It was rich!

Of the various rapid passages in the development section (beginning after m. 135) [Liszt] said, "You must play that very impertinently and obtrusively, then it has the right effect. Only do it as if greatness were behind it."

And greatness there is behind this towering work. It stands as one of the grand heroic concerti of the nineteenth century, and deserves to emerge from its cocoon in the shadows to regain its rightful place among the great works for piano and orchestra.

—*Michael Norell*

To Ferdinand David

FOURTH CONCERTO

IN D MINOR
FOR PIANO & ORCHESTRA
OP. 70

Anton Rubinstein
1829-1894

Engraving: Wieslaw Novak

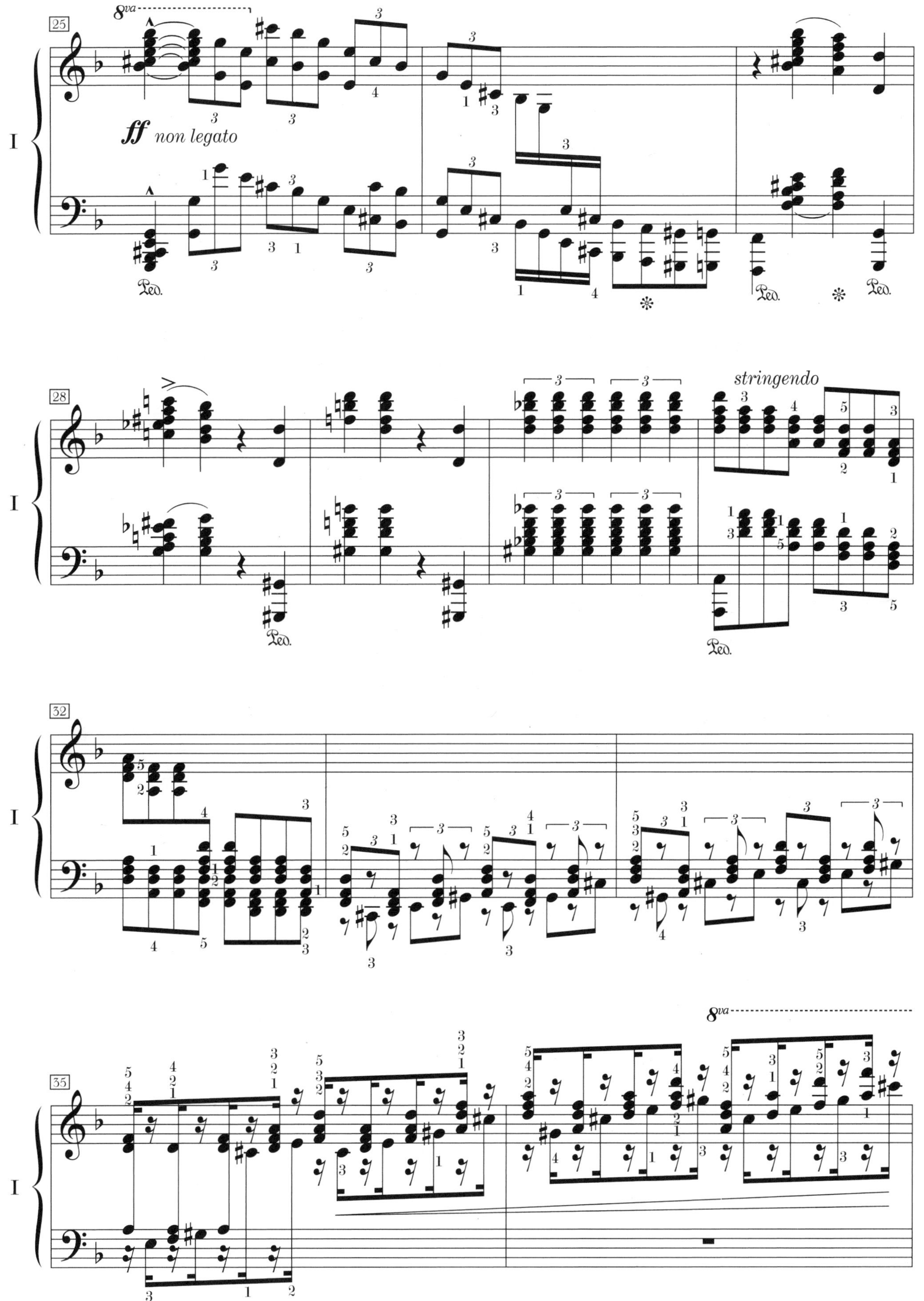
8va
ff non legato
I
Ped.
stringendo

(8va)
rit.
37
l.h.
l.h.
l.h.
32
Tempo I
A
tenuto
ff
tenuto
I
Tempo I
A
ff
II
41
I
45
33
tenuto
ff
tenuto
I
f
II

49
I
Ped.
Ped.
Ped.
II
53
Poco animato
mp
con espressione
Ped.
Ped.
Ped.
f
Poco animato
57
Ped.
Ped.
p

61
I
II
cresc.
Ped.
Ped.
Ped.
cresc.
65
2
34
B
B
p
69
mf

73
I
II
mf
77
mf
81
mp
mp

85
I
II
f
p

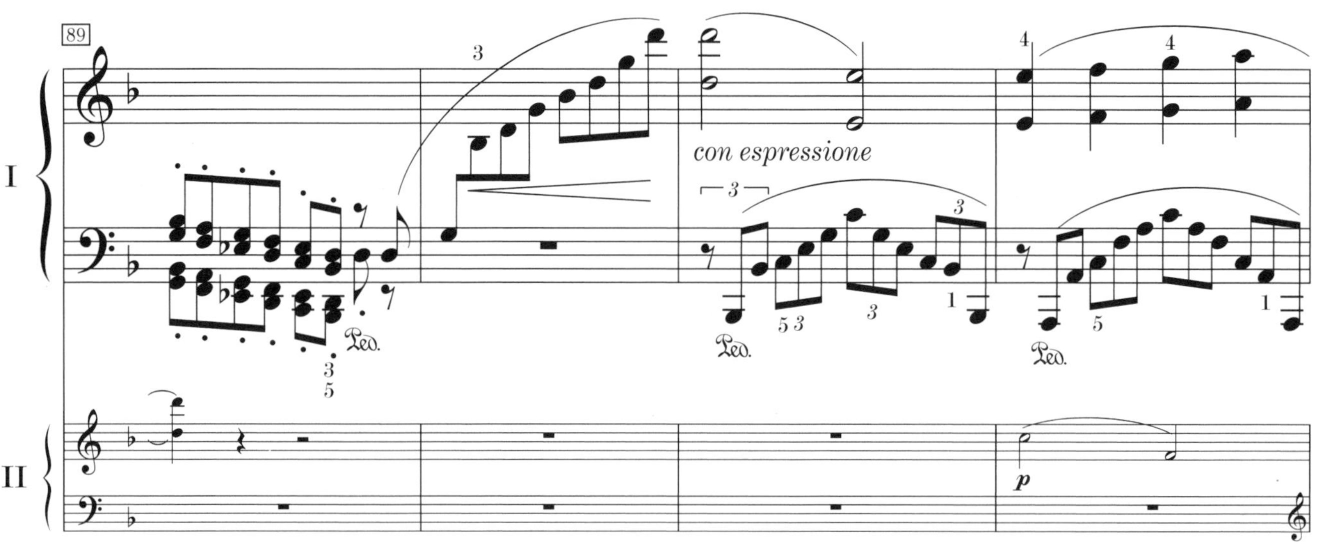
89
I
II
con espressione
p

93
I
II

96
I
II
Ped.
99
p
cresc.
rit.
102
a tempo
f
106

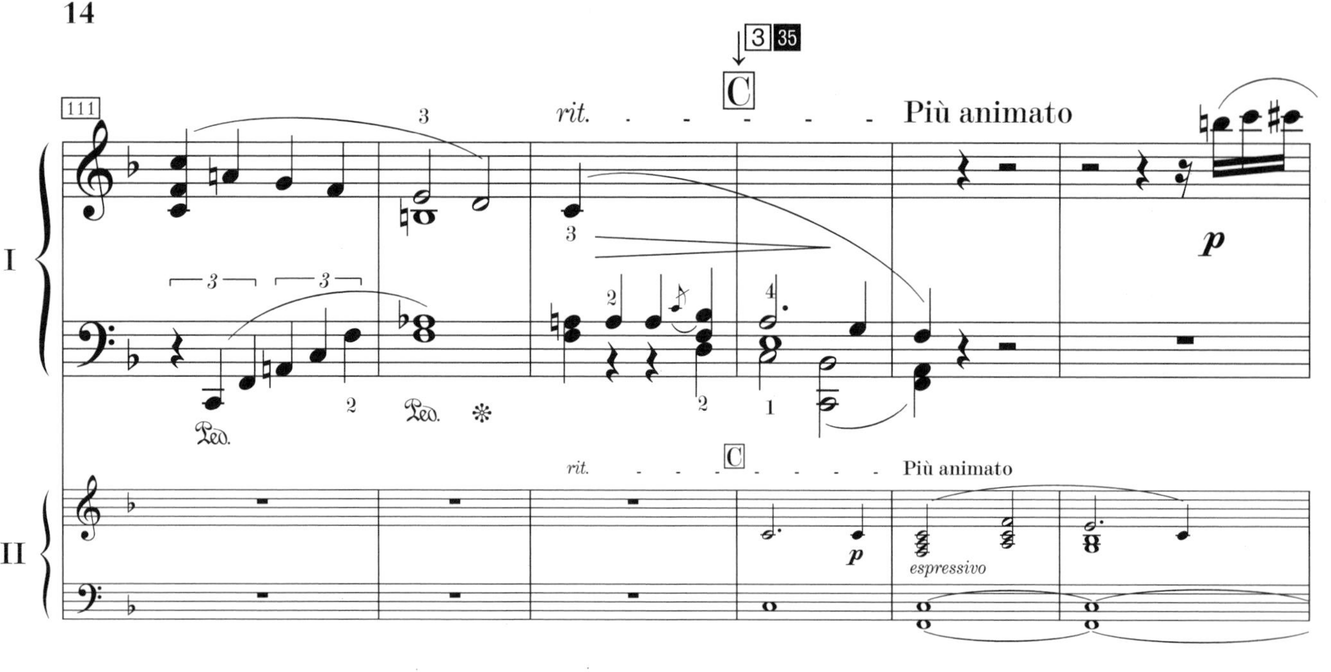
111
3 35
C
rit.
Più animato
I
II
espressivo

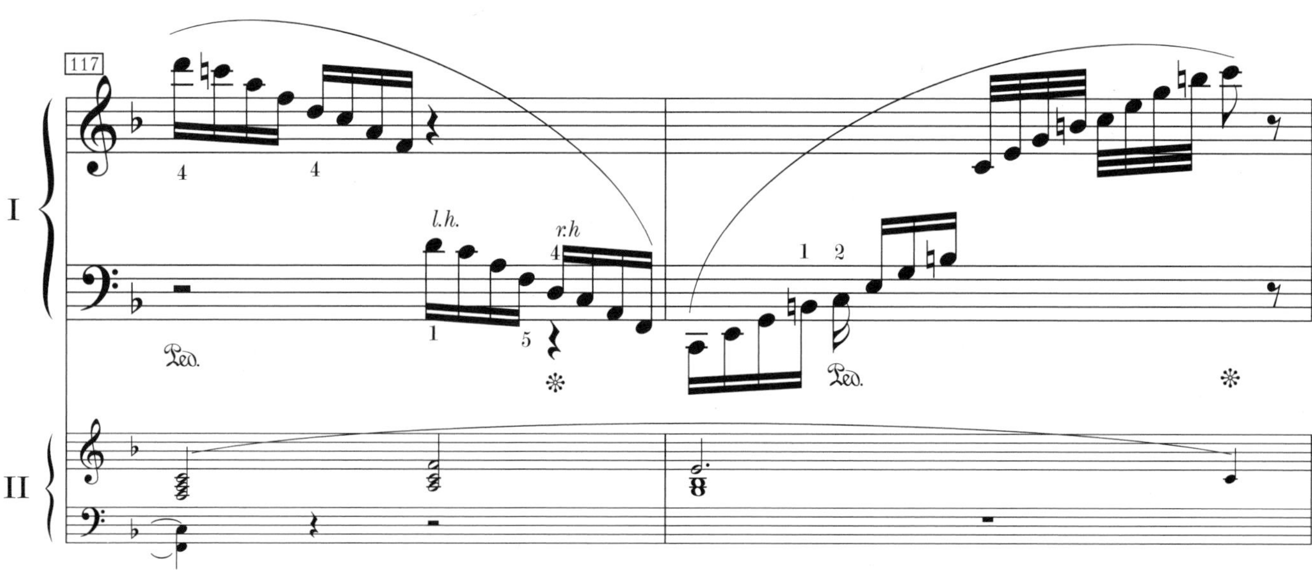
117
l.h.
r.h
I
II

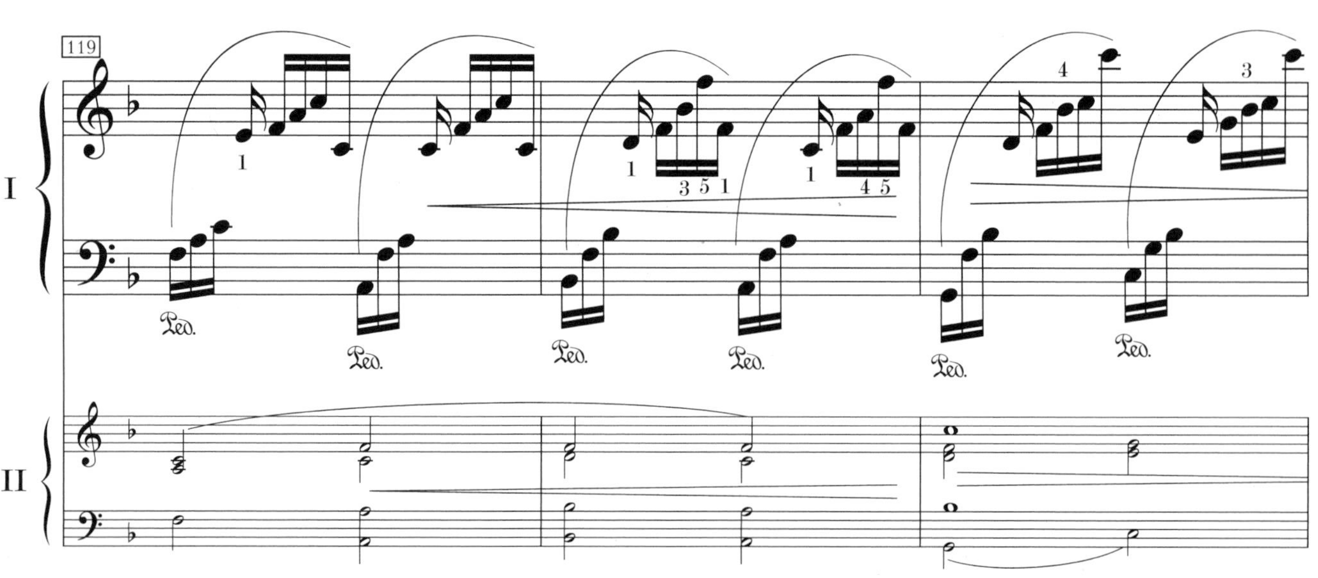
119
I
II

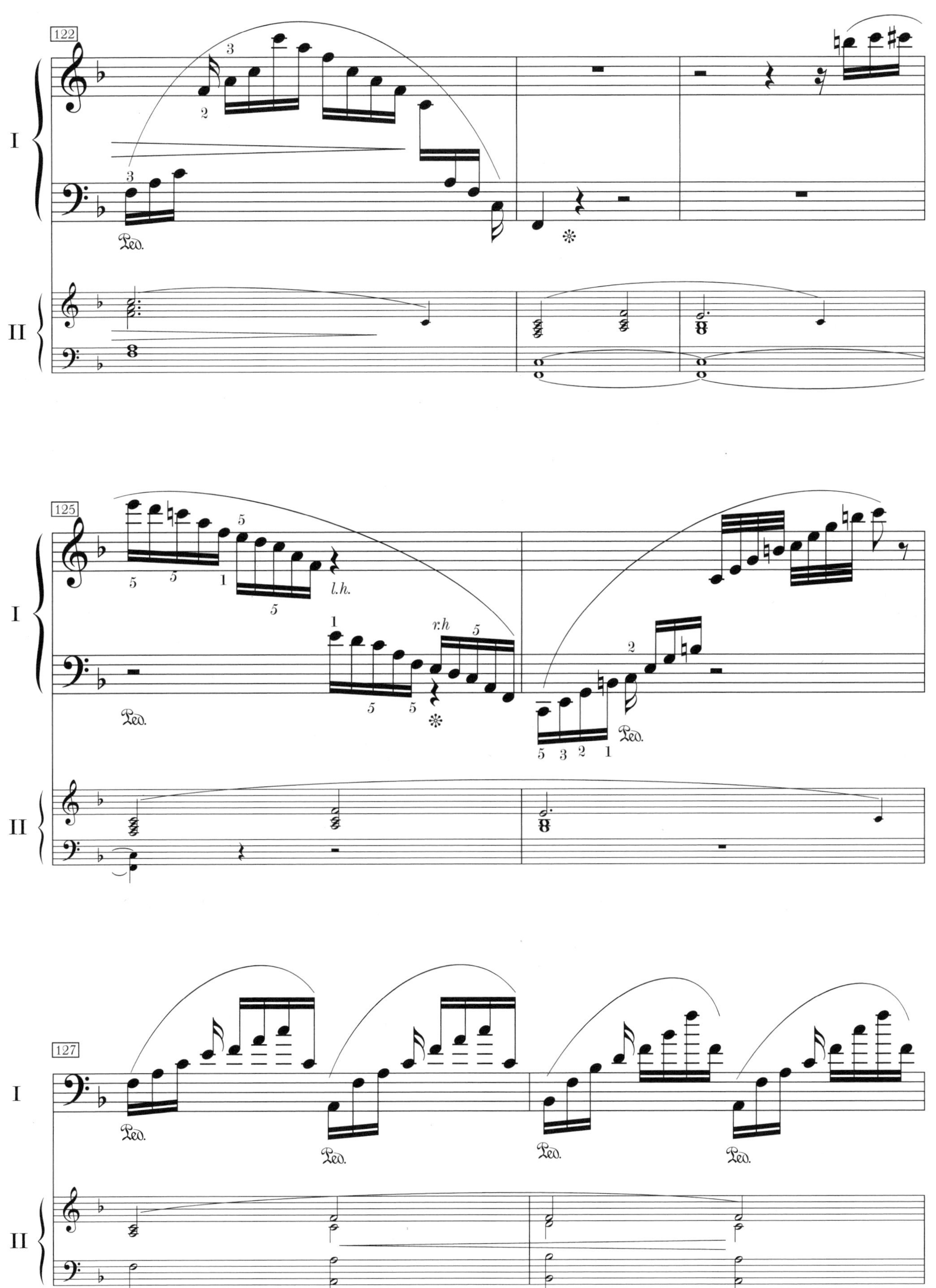
122
3
2
3
I
II
125
5
5
1
5
l.h.
5
1
r.h
5
5
5
2
5
3
2
1
127

129
I
II
Ped.
f
132
8va
rit.
4 36
Tempo I
ff
(8vb)
p
136
mp

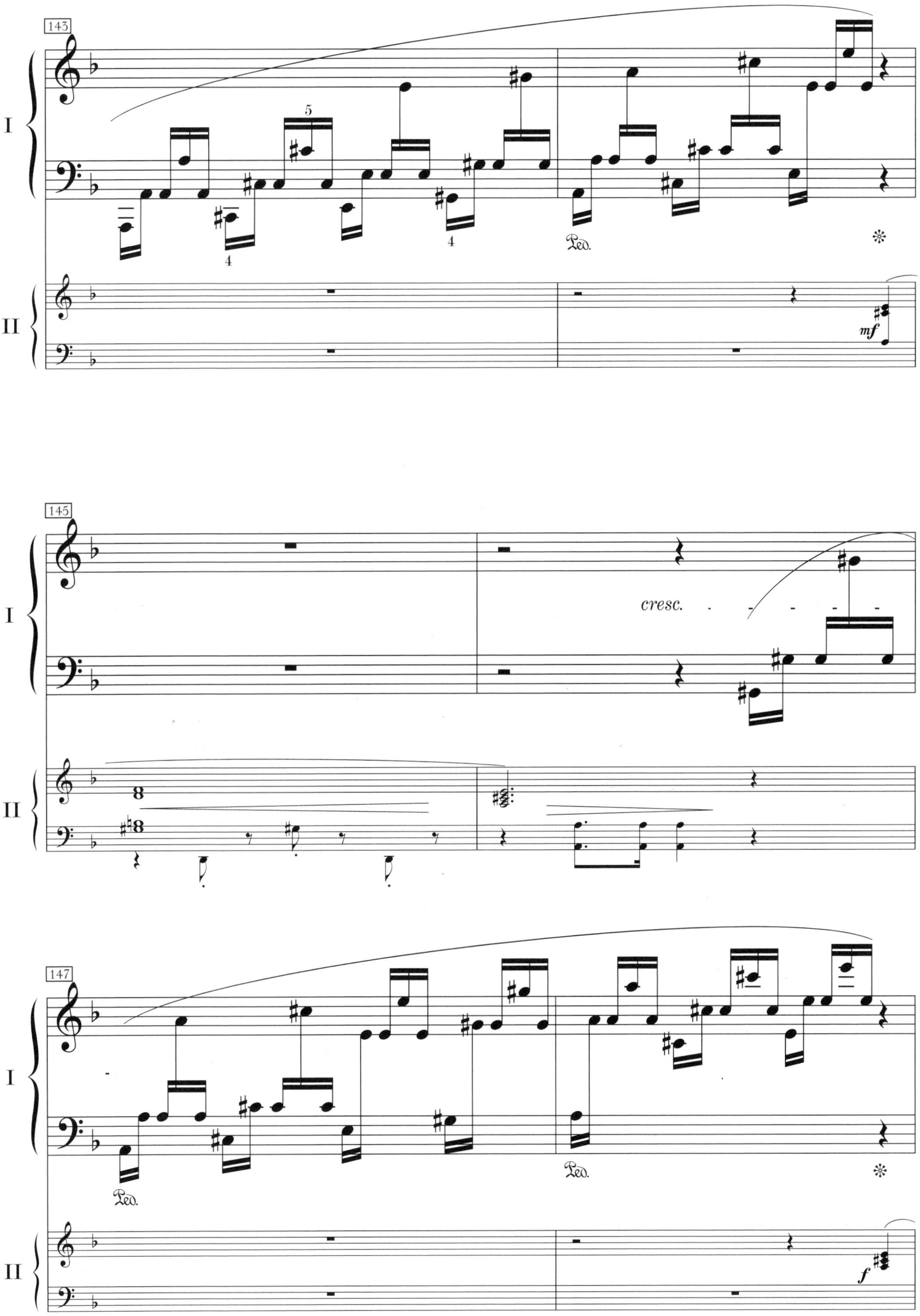

145

I

cresc.

II

147

I

Ped.

Ped.

II

f

149
Animato
I
II
p
Animato
p
152
I
II
espressivo
154
I
II
cresc.
3

156
I
II
Ped.
3
158
f
cresc.
160

162
I
dim.
Ped.
3
II
dim.
164
I
Ped.
3
II
3
8va
5 37
Tempo I
166
D
I
p
Ped.
Tempo I
D
II
p
3

170
I
II
175
Animato
mf legato sempre
178
181
p
Ped.
184
Ped.
Ped.
Ped.

187
I
Ped.
190
Ped.
193
pp
196
E
II
p

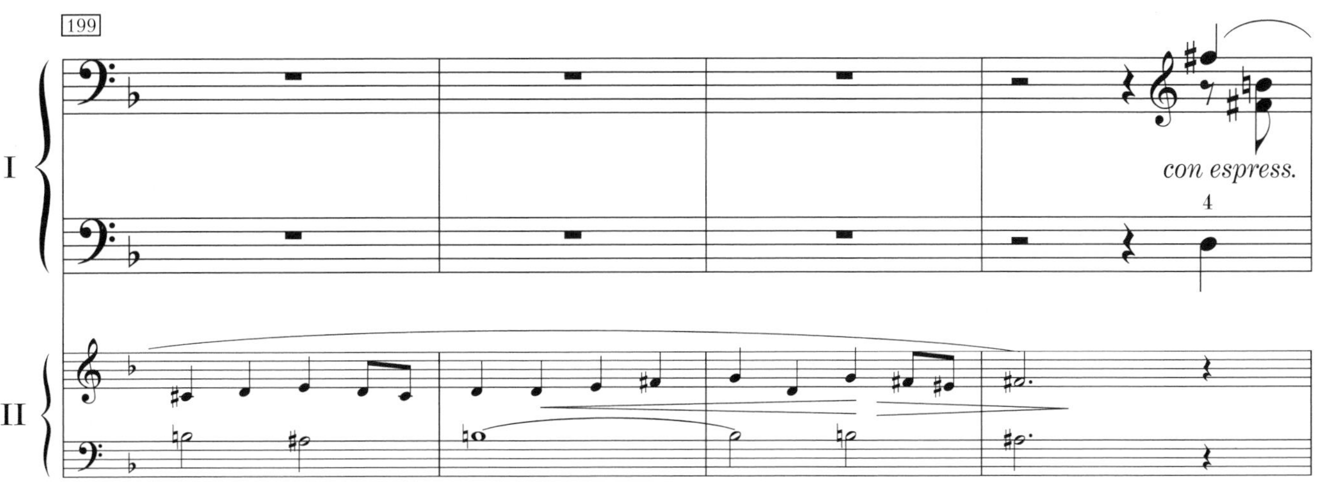
199
I
II
con espress.

203
I
II
cresc.

207
I
II
cresc.

212
I
II
poco a poco accel.
mf
poco a poco accel.
216
mf
cresc.
220
cresc.
f
f

224
I
II
228
più accel.
Ped.
231
f
Ped.

234

I

Ped. Ped.

II

237

7 39

F

ff

I

Ped. Ped.

II

F

ff

244
8va
I
Ped.
Ped.
sf
II
f
247
1 5
f
Ped.
Ped.
251
f
legato sempre
Ped.
Ped.

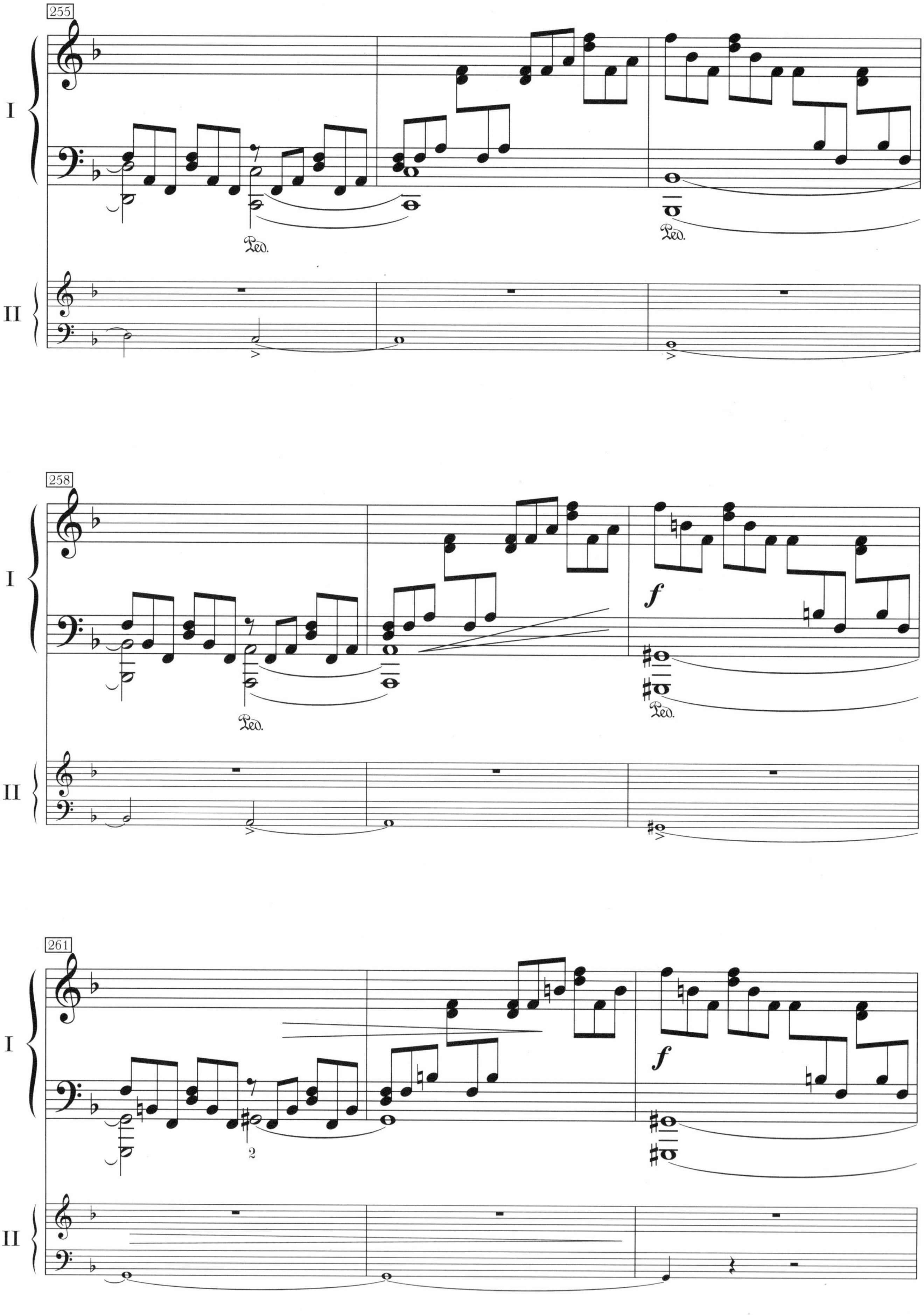
255
I
Ped.
Ped.
II
258
I
f
Ped.
Ped.
II
261
I
2
f
II

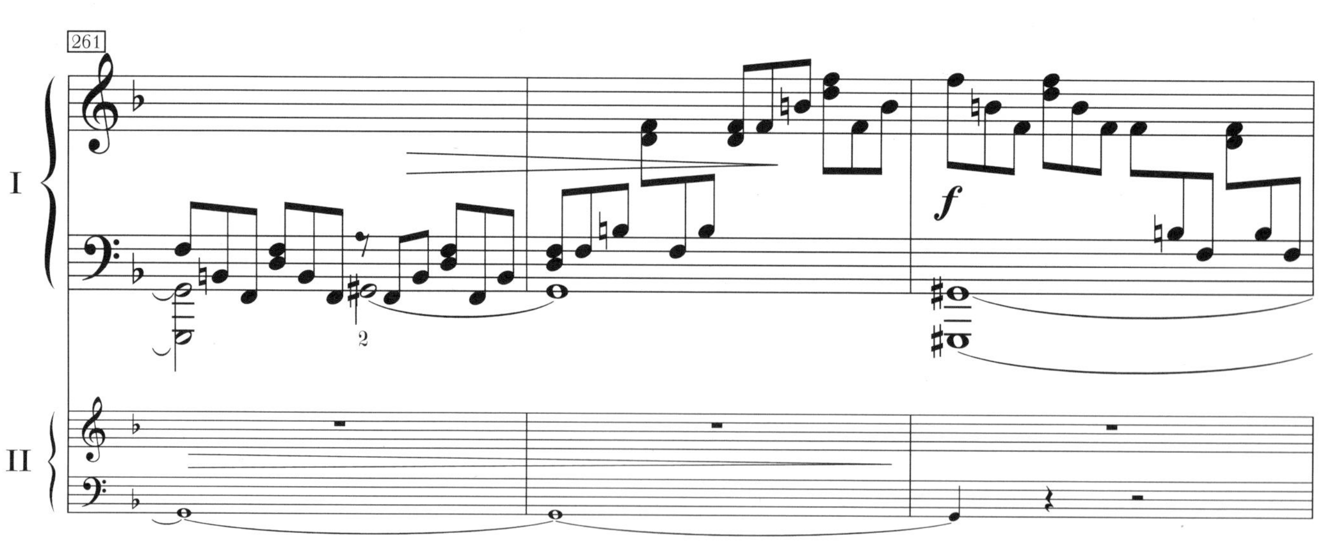

264
calmando
ritard.
I
mf
Ped.
calmando
ritard.
II
267
I
Ped.
Ped.
II
270
a tempo
I
Ped.
Ped.
a tempo
II

273
I
II
276
I
Ped.
Ped.
I
I
8va

8va
p
8vb
8 40
Tempo I
I
II
Tempo I
p
281
cresc.
286
poco a poco sempre animato
mf
290
f

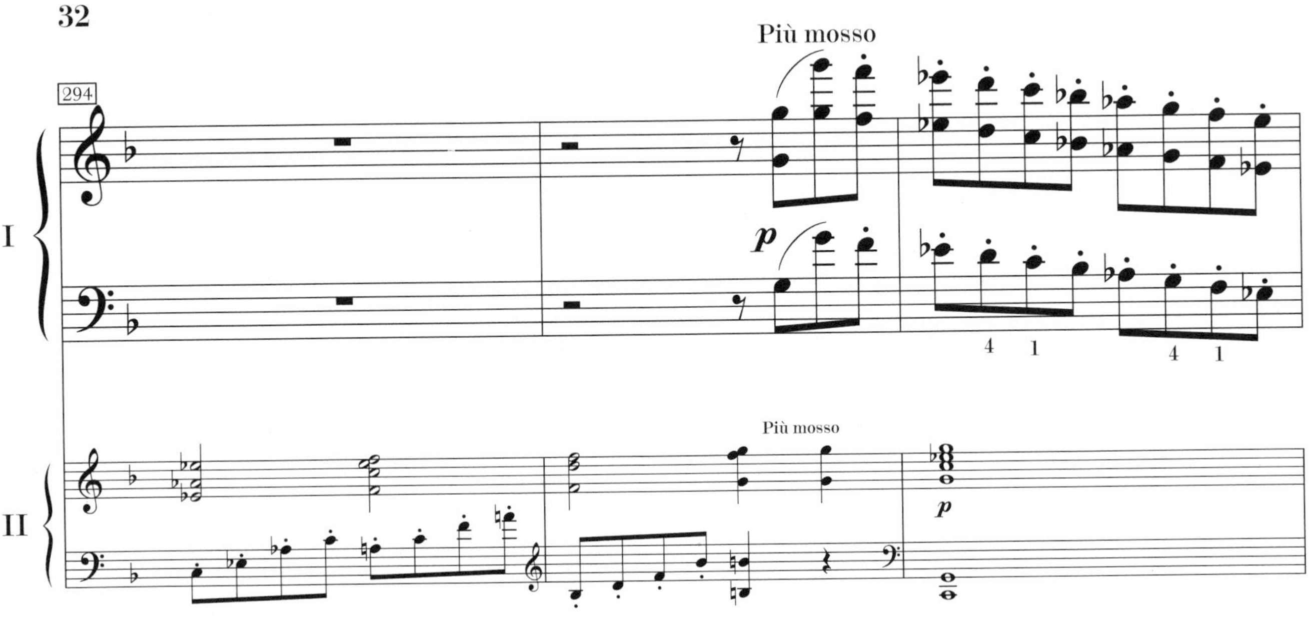
Più mosso
294
I
II
p
Più mosso
p

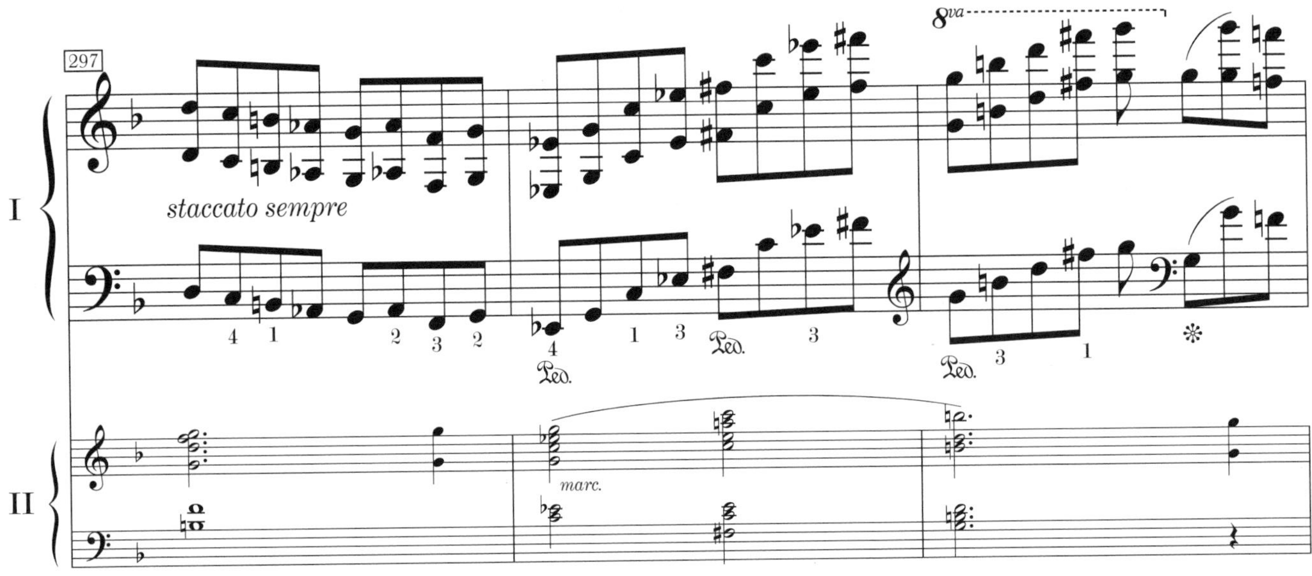
297
I
II
staccato sempre
8va
marc.

300
I
II

303 8va cresc. Ped. p

I

II

306 f

I

II

309 ritard. Ped.

I

II

ritard.

Tempo I
312
f appassionato
I
II
Tempo I
mp
316
320
ritard.
323
rit.
f

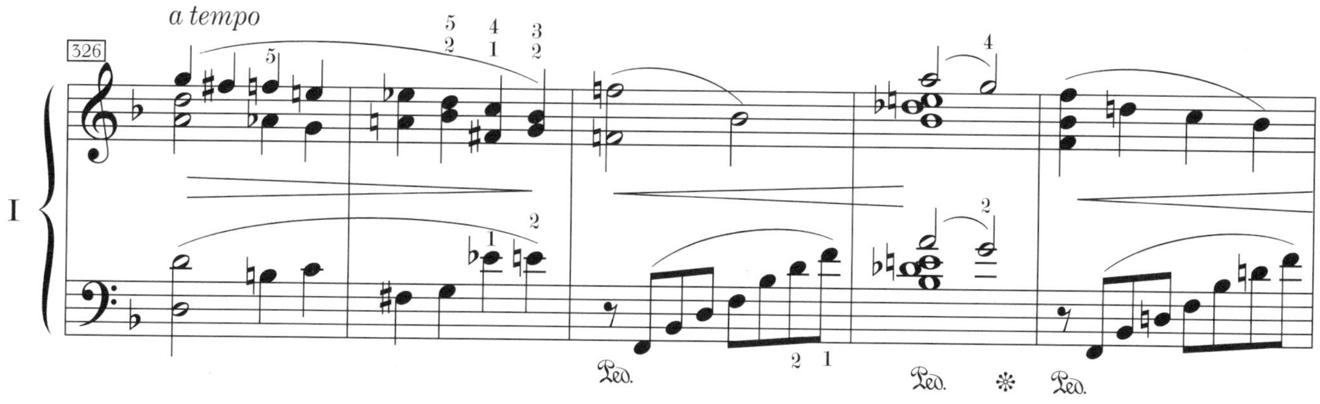
a tempo
326
I
Ped.
Ped.
Ped.

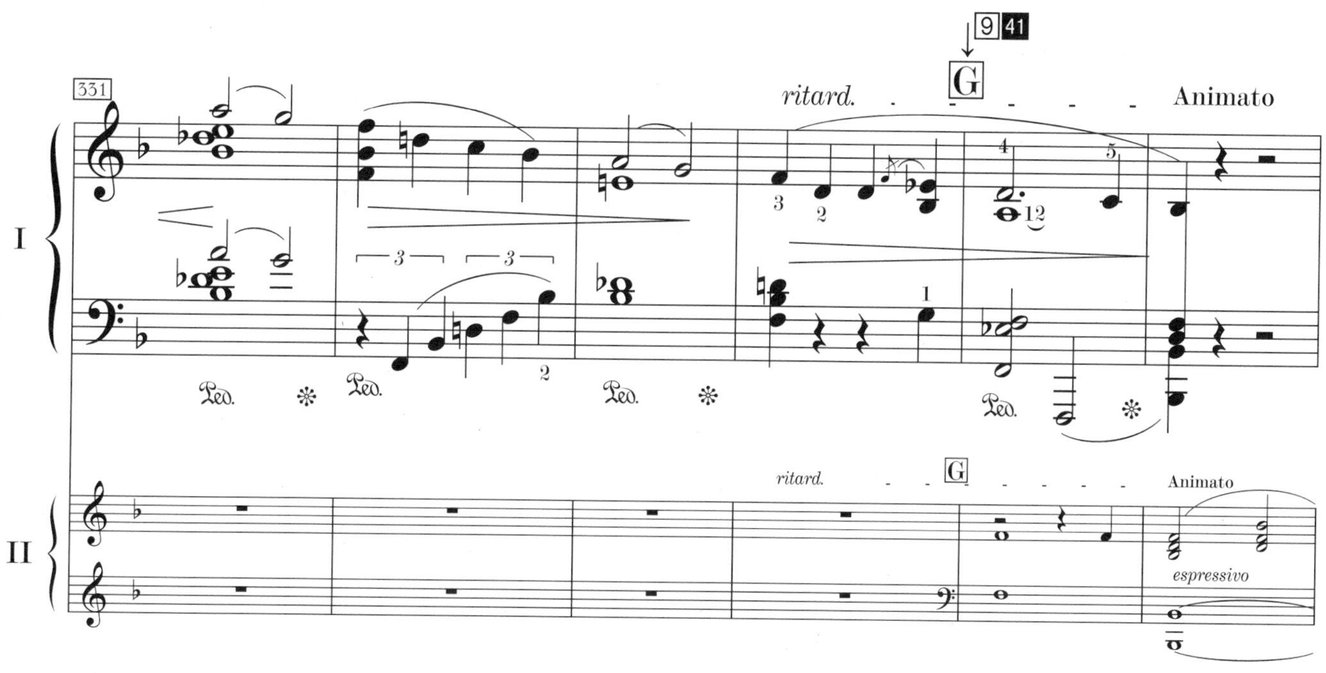
331
9 41
G
ritard.
Animato
I
Ped.
Ped.
Ped.
Ped.
II
ritard.
G
Animato
espressivo

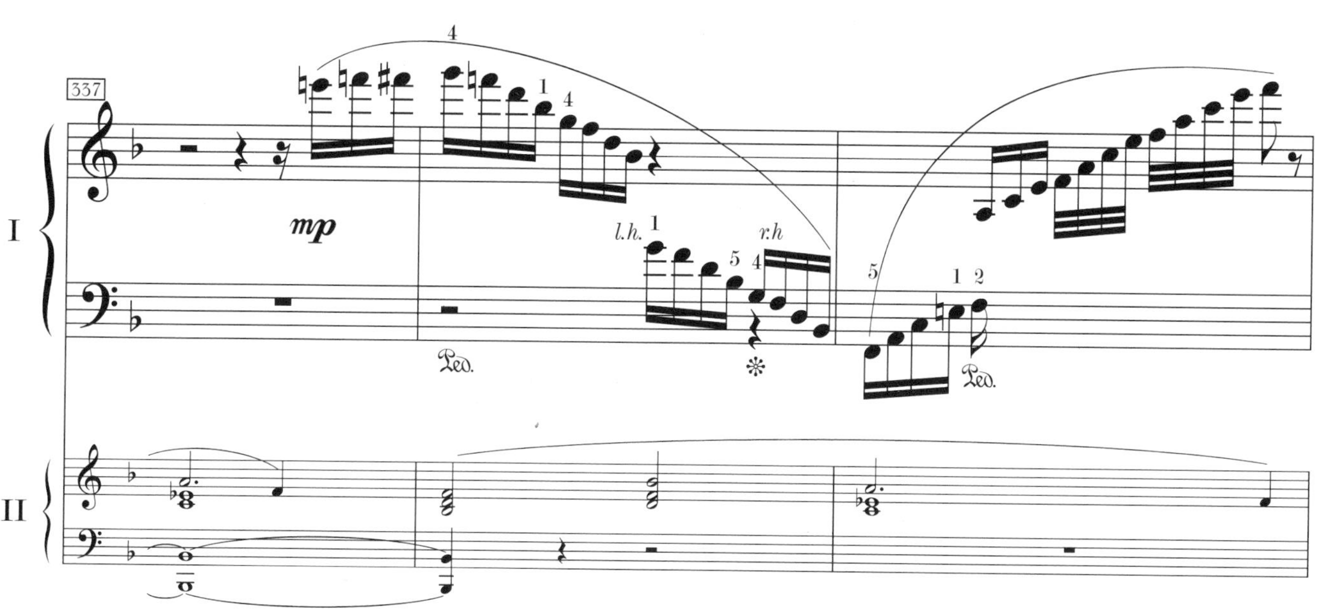
337
I
mp
l.h.
r.h
Ped.
Ped.
II

340
I
II
343
I
II
346
I
II

348
I
II
Ped.
351
ff
f
mf
354
r.h
l.h.

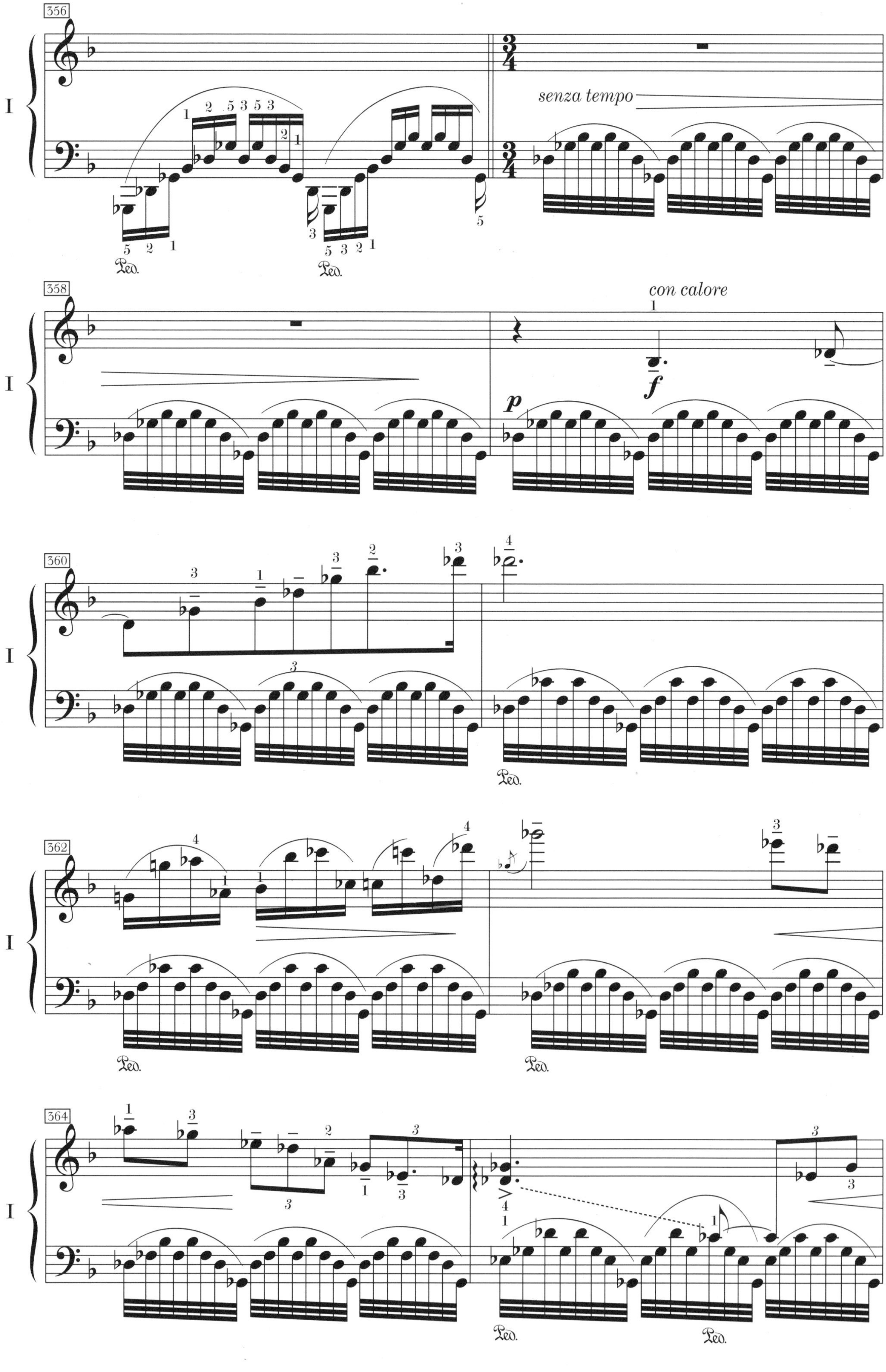

356

I

senza tempo

Ped. Ped.

358

I

con calore

360

I

Ped.

362

I

Ped. Ped.

364

I

Ped. Ped.

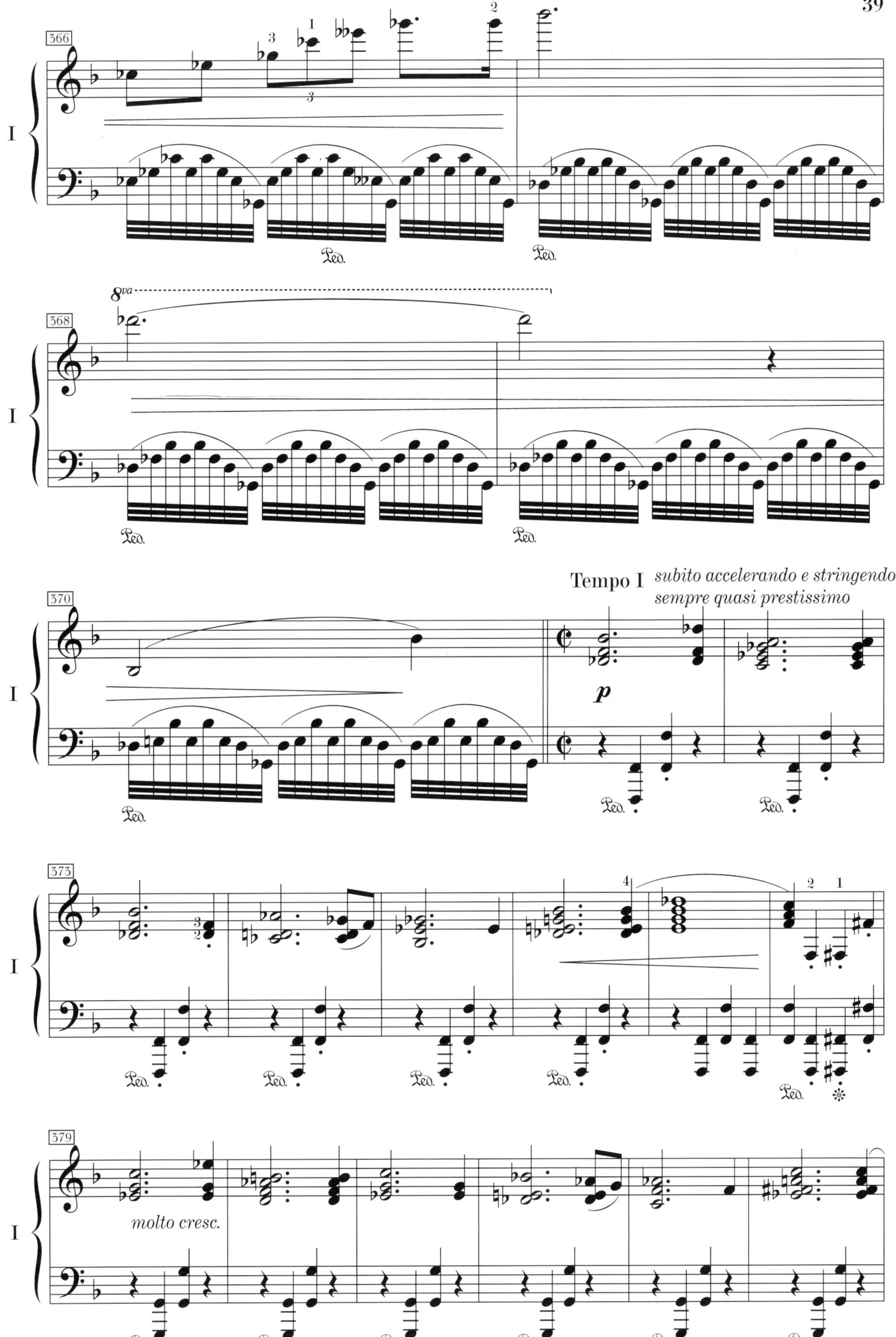
366
I
Ped.
Ped.
368
I
Ped.
Ped.
370
I
Ped.
Tempo I
subito accelerando e stringendo
sempre quasi prestissimo
p
Ped.
Ped.
373
I
Ped.
Ped.
Ped.
Ped.
Ped.
379
I
molto cresc.
Ped.
Ped.
Ped.
Ped.
Ped.
Ped.

385
I
2 1
f
Ped.
Ped.
Ped.
Ped.
Ped.

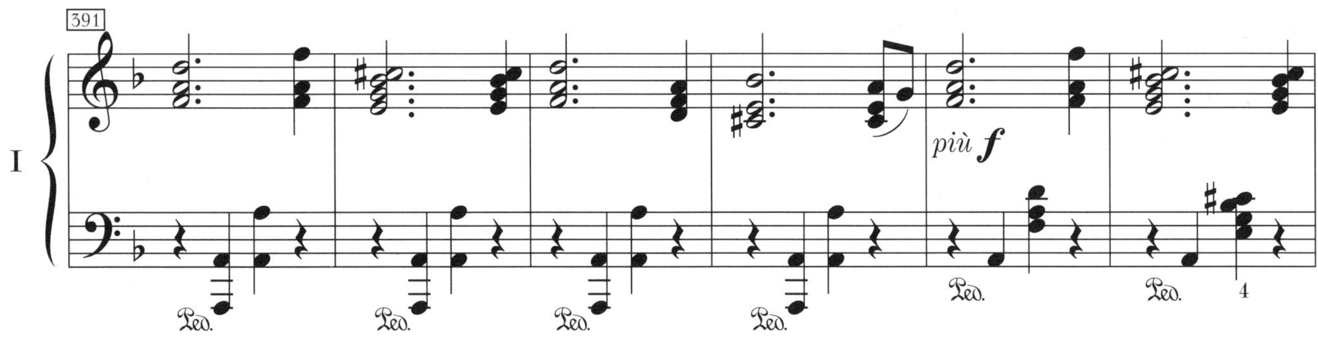
391
I
più f
Ped.
Ped.
Ped.
Ped.
Ped.
Ped.
4

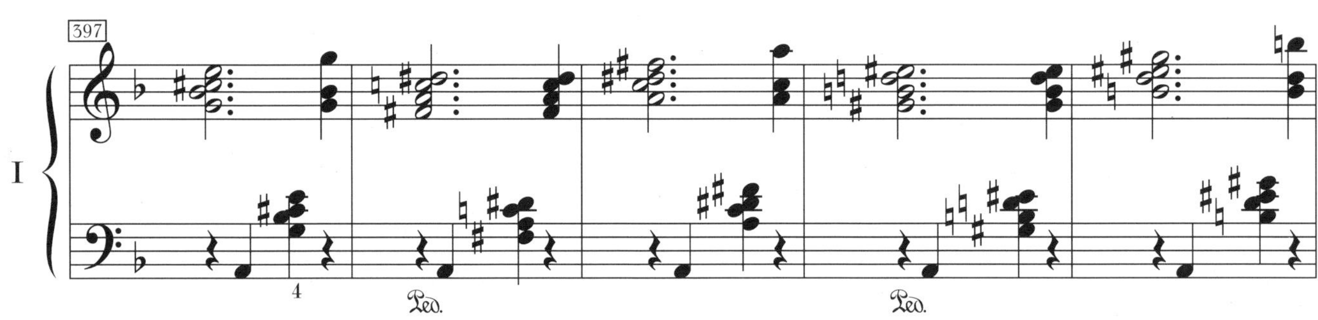
397
I
4
Ped.
Ped.

402
I
8va
Ped.

408
(8va)
I
4 4
ff
Ped.

413
(8va)
I
ff sempre e tumultuoso
418
423
ritard.
429
8va
10 42
Tempo I
fff
Ped.
Ped.
Tempo I
f
II

433
I
II
436
I
II
439
I
II

442
8va
8va
I
II
Ped.
Ped.
445
I
II
Ped.
447
Allegro (= 𝅗𝅥)
mf
I
Ped.
Allegro (= 𝅗𝅥)
p
II

451
I
cresc.
Ped.
5
sim.
II
cresc.
455
pp
Ped.
pp
459
sim.

463
H
animato
I
mf
Ped.
II
p
467
cresc.
l.h.
471
Ped.

475
I
II
478
8va
ff
Ped.
f
481
8va
Ped.
Ped.

484
I
II
Ped.
487
stringendo
490
cresc.

493
a tempo
ff
I
II
496
8va
Ped.
mf
f
500

II.

11 43
Andante (= ♩)
I
II
Andante (= ♩)
p
cresc.
8
meno mosso
a tempo
mf
Ped.
meno mosso
a tempo
12
con molto espressione

17

I

sopra

21

44

I

cresc.

II

25

I

II

30

I

33
I
l.h.
r.h
Ped.
37
12 45
A
Un poco animato
II
42
46

49
I
52
I
Ped.
55
I
mf
58
46
ritard.
II
ritard.
mp

62
I
II
Ped.
66
47
Tempo I
B
con molta espressione
Tempo I
Fl.
70

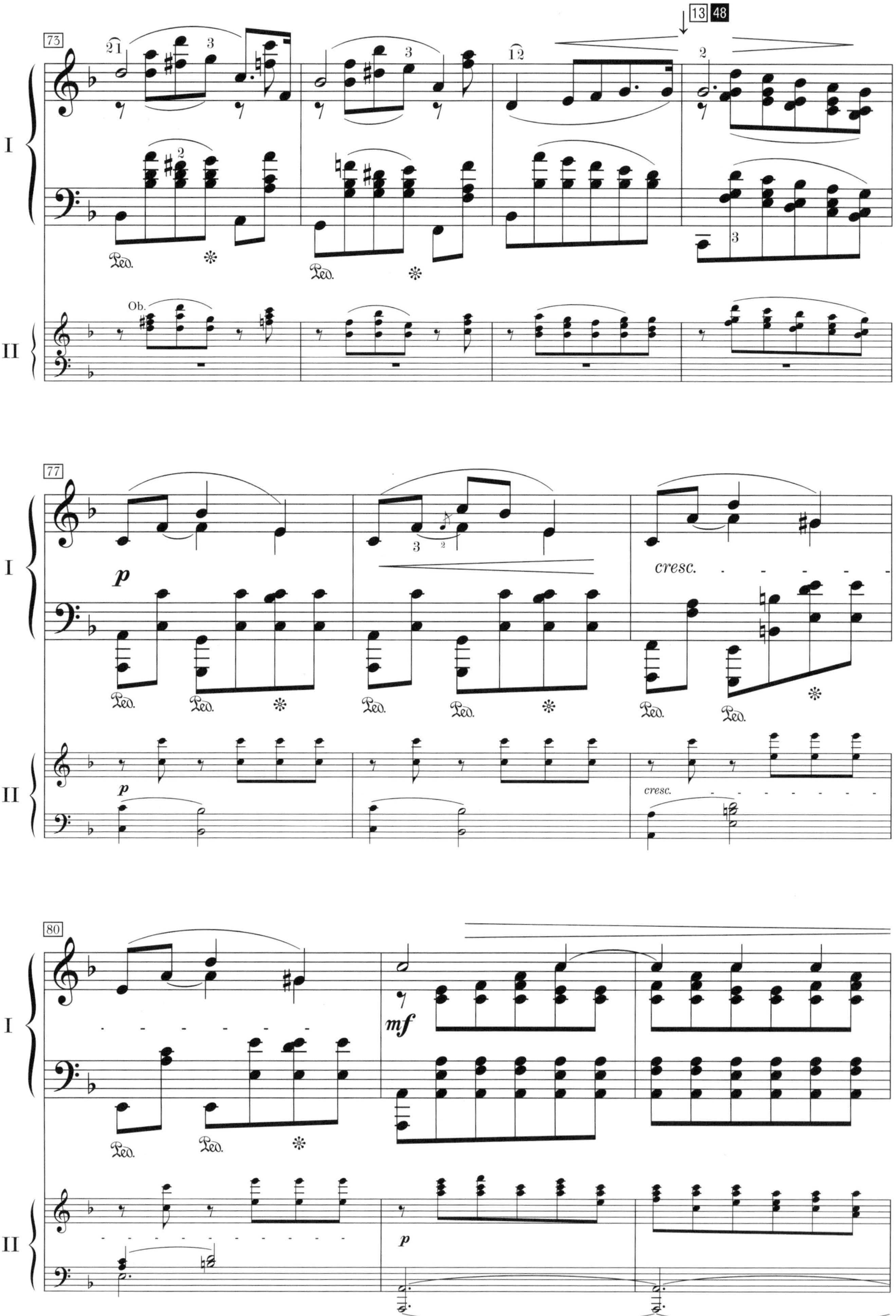

73 13 48

I

II

Ob.

77

p

cresc.

80

mf

p

83
I
II
mf
88
49
f
l.h.
r.h
p
93
14
50
Con moto
Con moto
mf
p

97

I

sempre legato

100

I

103

I

51

C

mf

l.h.

II

C

mf

106

I

II

109
I
II
112
I
II
115
f
I
f
II

118
I
II
121
poco a poco accel.
mf
cresc.
124
f

127
I
II
4
p
130
4
3
5
3
133
15
52
3
5
cresc.
4

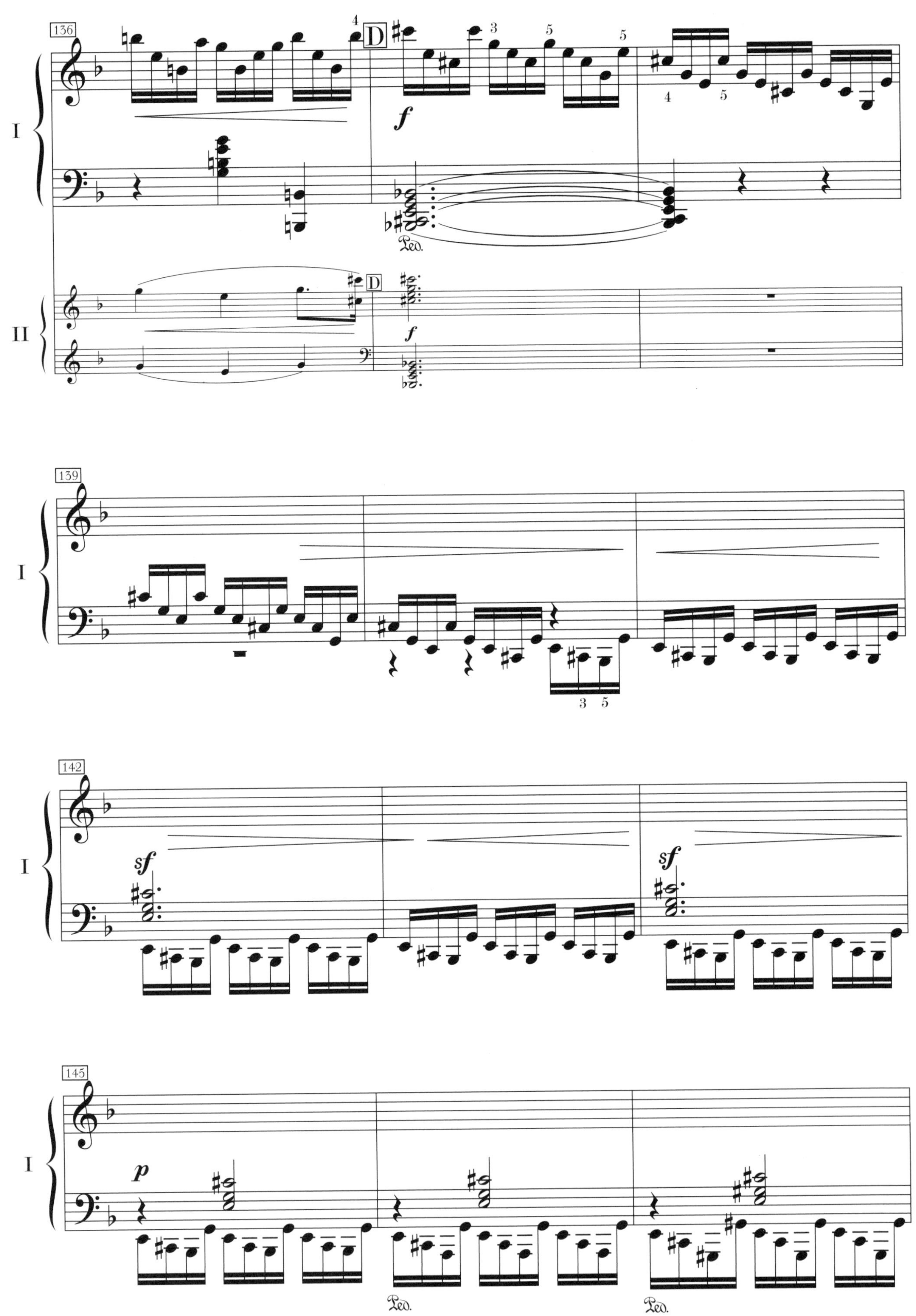
136
D
f
I
II
139
142
sf
145
p
Ped.

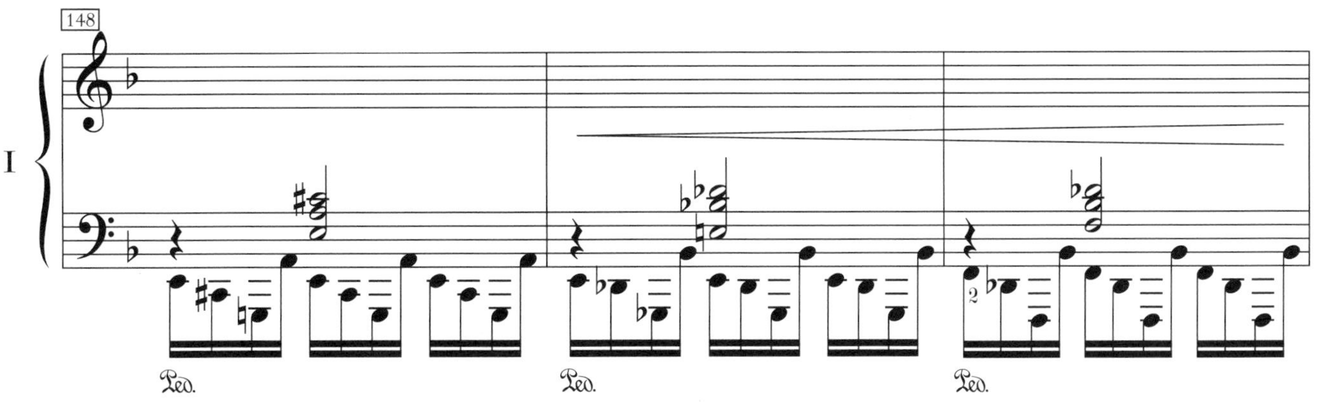
148
I
Ped.
Ped.
Ped.

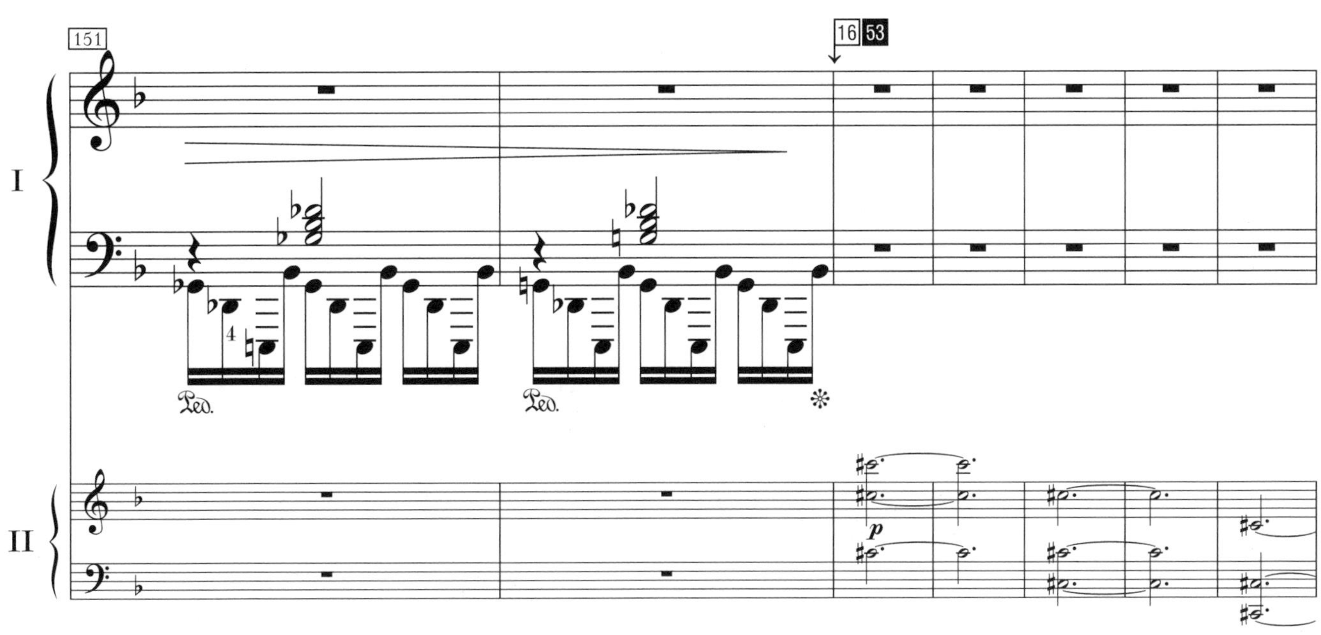
151
16 53
I
II
Ped.
Ped.
p

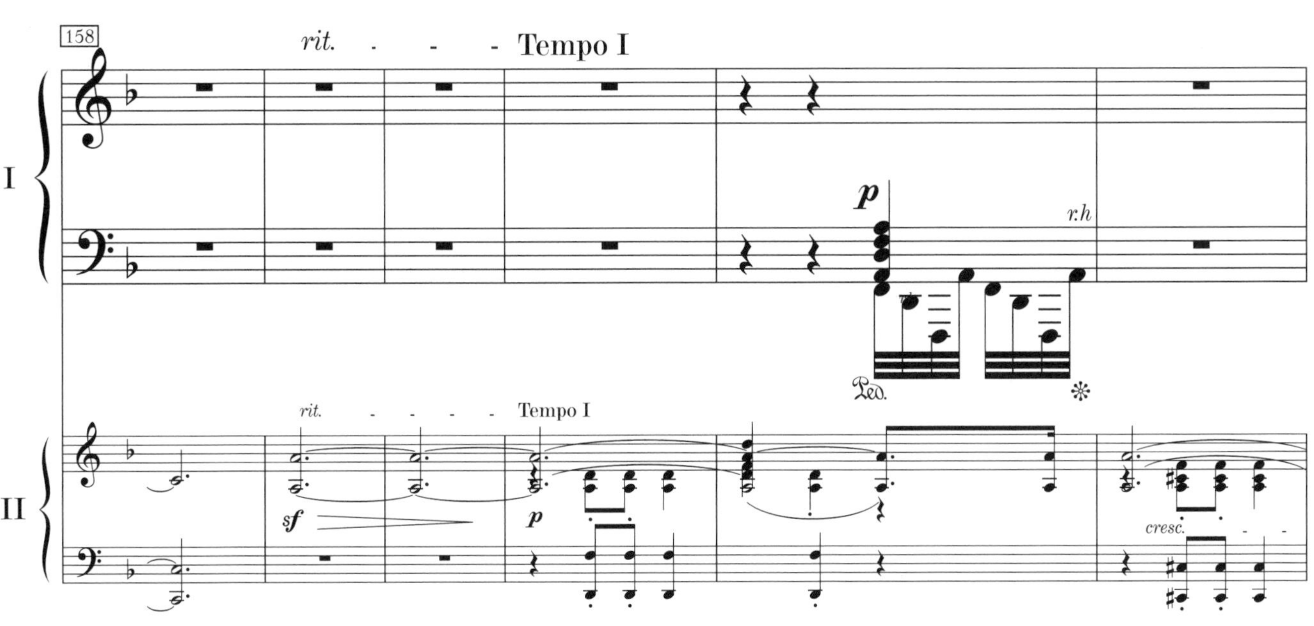
158
rit. - - - - Tempo I
I
II
p
r.h
Ped.
rit. - - - - Tempo I
sf
p
cresc. - - -

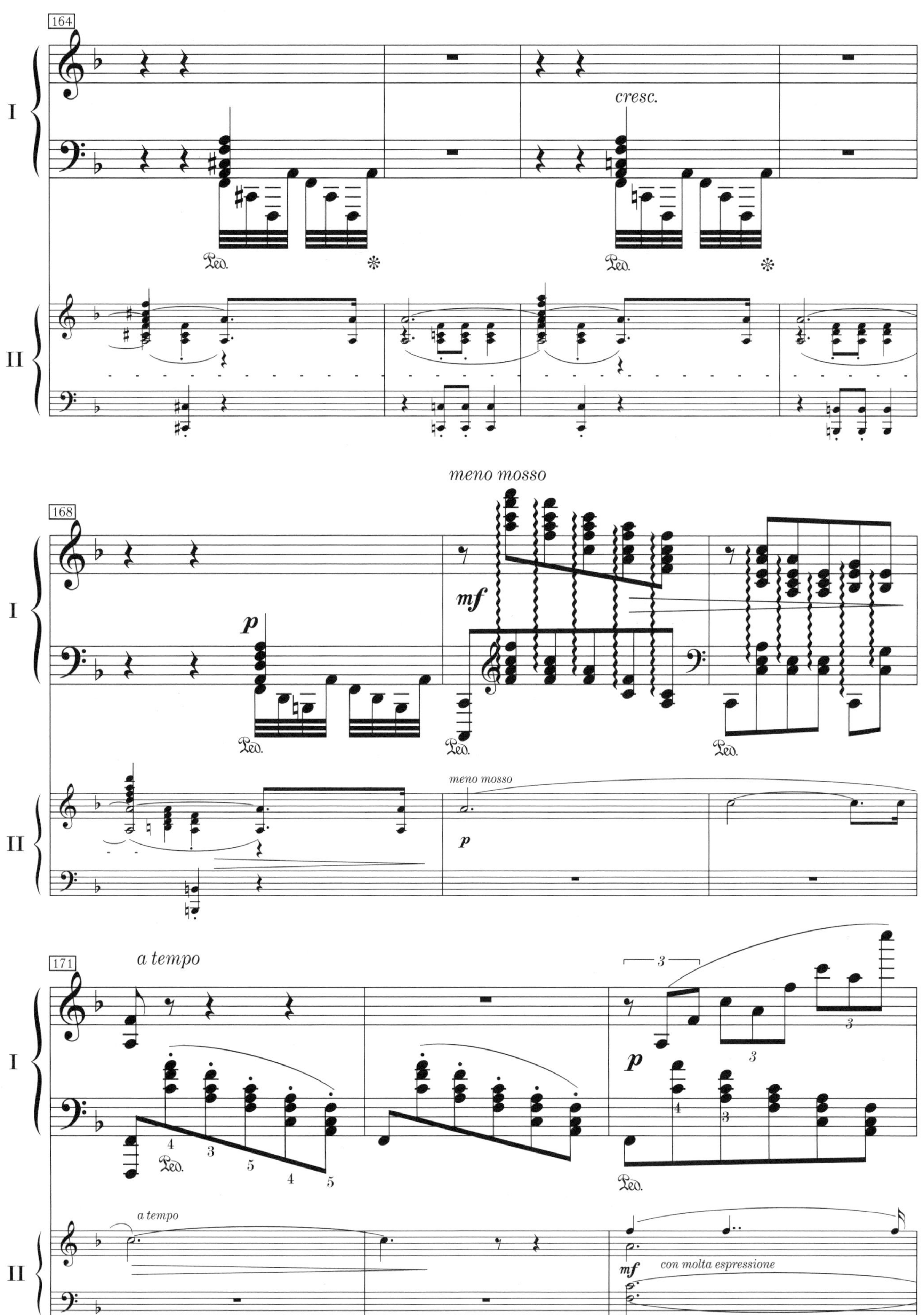
164
I
cresc.
Ped.
II
168
meno mosso
p
mf
171
a tempo
con molta espressione
mf

174
I
II
Ped.
Ped.
Ped.
177
Ped.
Ped.
Ped.
Ped.
Ped.
180
8va
8va
Ped.
Ped.
Ped.
Ped.
Ped.

183
I
II
mf
186
17 54
8vb
Cl.
189

192
I
II
196
200
E
MMO 3079

205 I II l.h. l.h. l.h. r.h
mf *sf p* Ped. Ped. Ped. Ped.

211 55 *p* *pp* *pp* r.h Ped. Ped.

216 8va

III.

29
I
f
33
I
Ped.
37
I
19 57
41
A
8va
II
ff
46
II
f
8va

Un poco animato
Un poco animato
mf
p
f
mf
f
II
I
II
I
I
I

73 58 B

I

mp legg.

II

B

82
I
II
85
8va
f
Ped.
sf
88
(8va)
20 59
ff
8va
f
Ped.

94
I
II
99
104
Ped.

21 60
8va
110
I
II
mp
f
115
122
125

128
I
131
I
Ped.
134
8va
C
I
f
Ped.
Ped.
137
61
8va
mp
I
Ped.
II
p

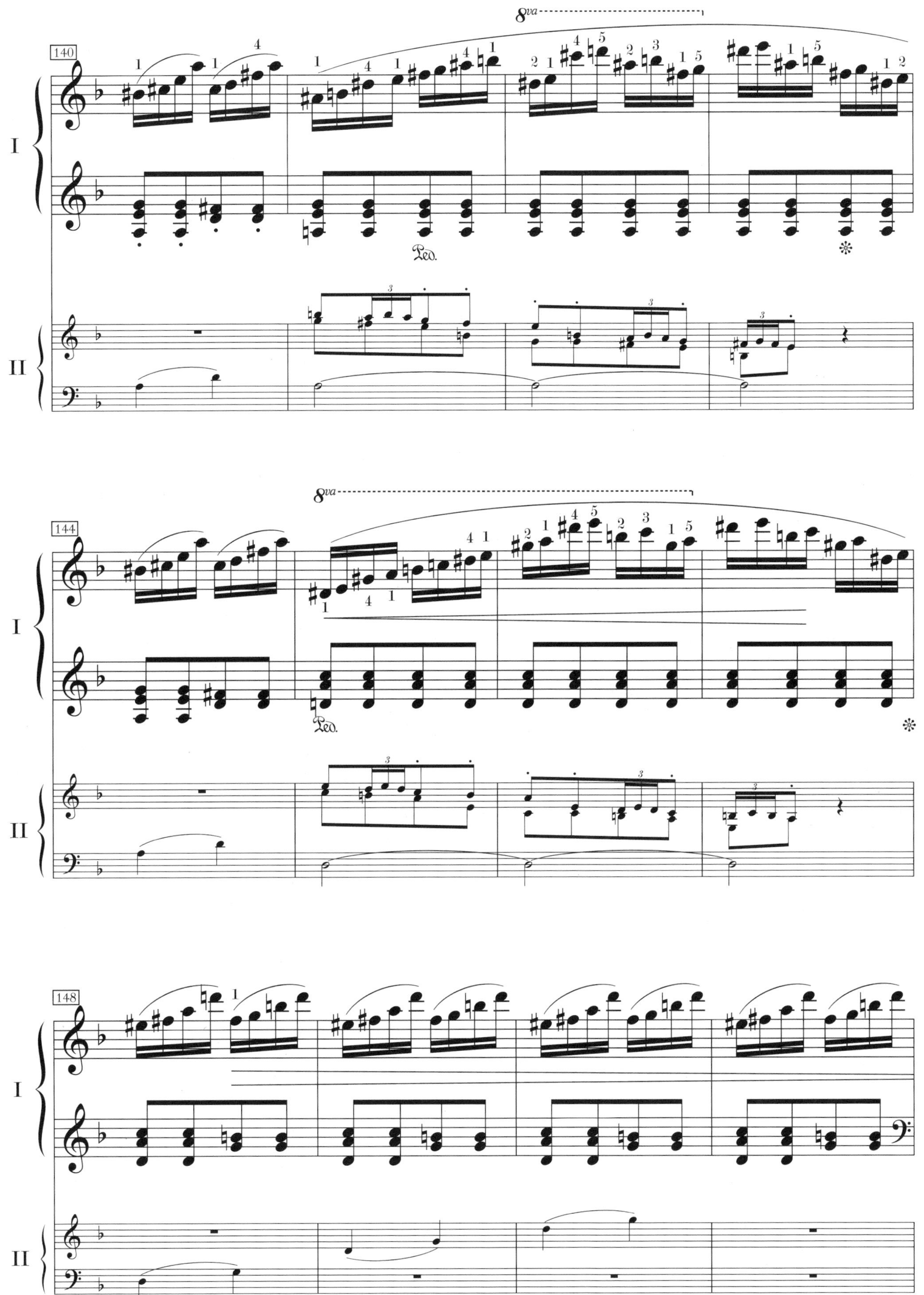

140
8va
I
II
Ped.
144
8va
148

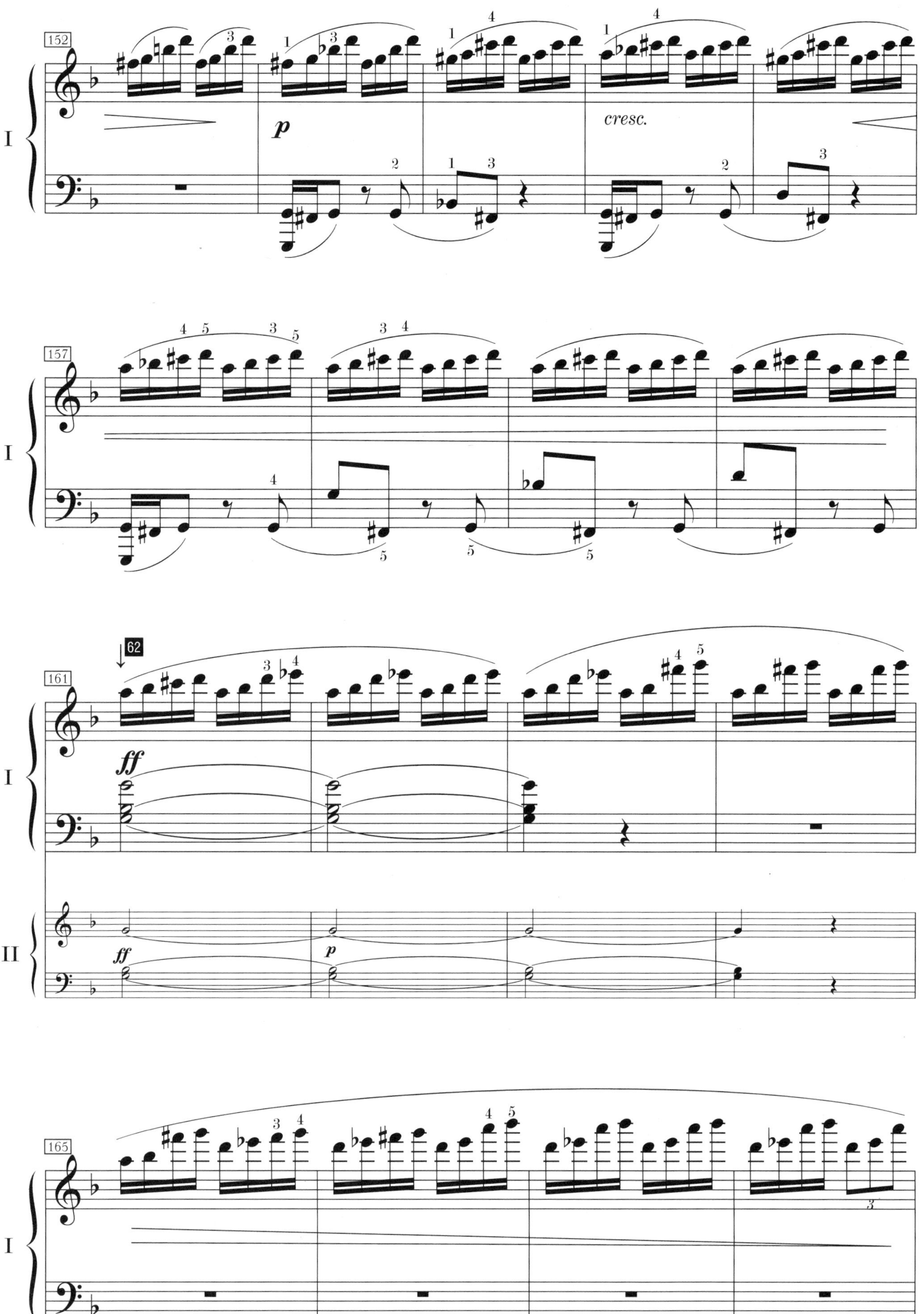
152
I
p
cresc.
157
I
161
62
ff
I
II
ff
p
165
I

63
169
I
p
Ped.
II
Fg.
173
f
177
Ped.
Cl.
mf

181
I
22 64
Tempo I
185
II
ff
189
f
195
D
200
Animato assai
Animato assai
Tpts.
sf
Ob.

207
I
II
Hrn.
sf
Hrn.
sf
Cl.
sf
214
dim.
Ob.
sf
dim.
Ob.
sf
Cl.
220
p
Fl.
Fl.
p
Fg.

226
I
II
Fg.
Fl.
Fl.
Ob.
mf
Hrn.
233
mf
Vl.
p
241
mf

249
I
II
mf
cresc.
Fl.
mp
cresc.
256
f
Ped.
mf
263
p
con espressione
Ped.
Ped.
Ped.
Ped.

271
I
Ped.
279
E
287
23 65
Più animato
mf
II
Vl.
mp
295
cresc.

302
I
II
f
mp
Ped.
309
f
mf
15
Ped.
316
F
f
mf
Ped.

323
I
II
329
r.h
l.h.
335
f

341
I
II
347
353

359
G
I
II
p
Ped.
364
8va
369
(8va)

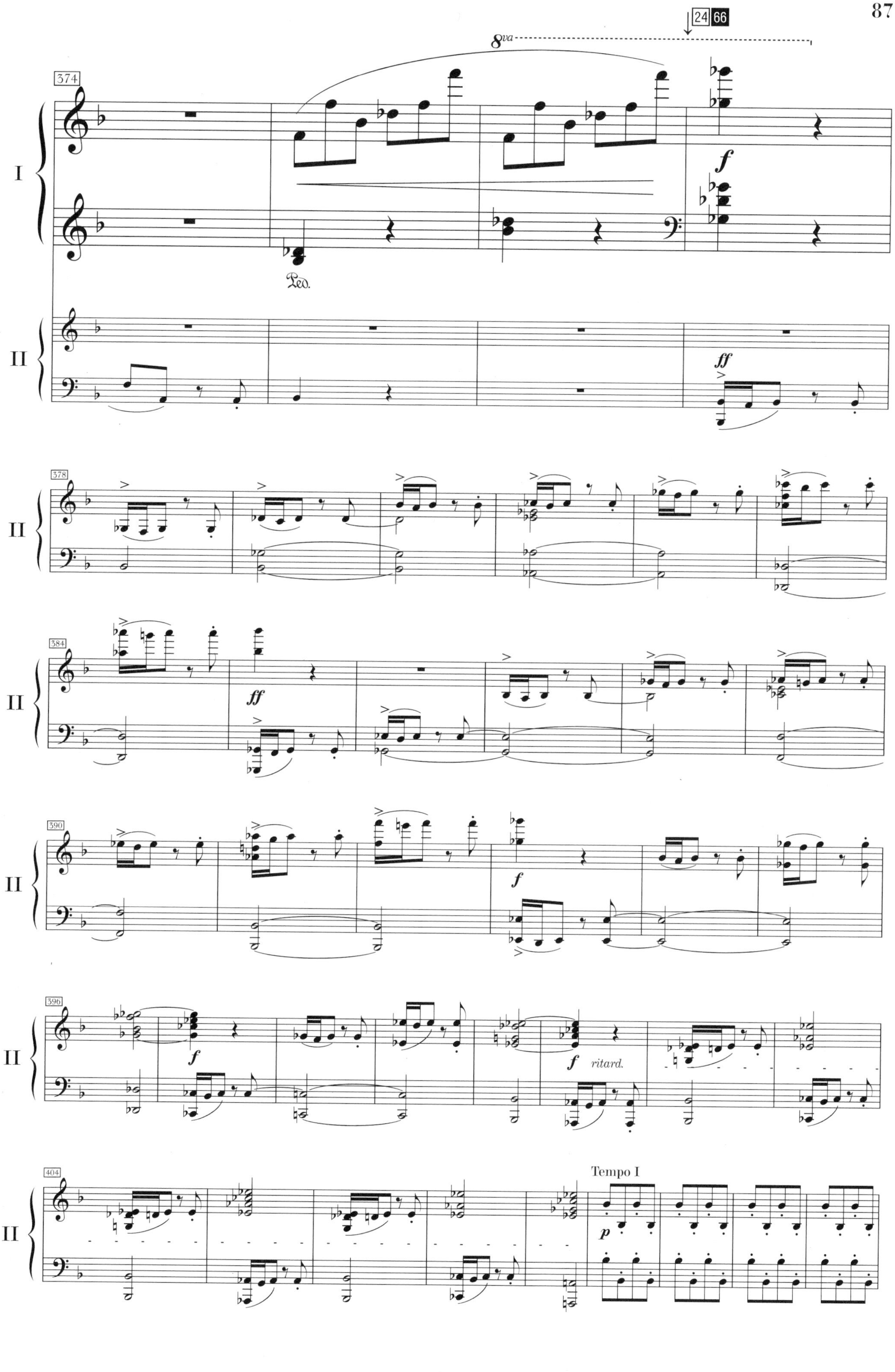
24 66
8va
374
I
Ped.
II
f
ff
378
384
390
396
ritard.
404
Tempo I
p

413
I
II
f
l.h.
418
424

429
f
p
Ped.
f
Ped.
434
438
f
Ped.
442
445
I

25 67
449
II
ff
455
f
461
I
Animato
GG
f
467
pp

471
I
II
476
480
f
mf

484
I
II
487
cresc.
cresc.
492
f

497
I
II
502
Più animato
8va
Ped.
Più animato
507
Ped.
Ped.

513

I

Ped. Ped. Ped. Ped.

520

I

Ped. Ped. Ped. Ped. Ped.

26 68

527 H

I

p

Ped.

8va

H

II

p

con espressione

535 (8va)

I

Ped. Ped.

II

543
Più animato
I
mp
II
p
Più animato
552
cresc.
558
mf
564
69
p
Ped.

571
I
mf
Ped.
II
578
f
sf
583
con espressione
p

589
I
II
595
f
601

607
I
II
sf
p
612
cresc.
617
27
70

622
K
Sempre più animato
I
f
Ped.
Ped.
Ped.
K
Sempre più animato
II
f
627
I
Ped.
II
f
632
I
Ped.
Ped.
Ped.
Ped.
Ped.
II

637
I
II
Ped.
f
643
648

653
I
II
𝒇
Ped.
658
663
sempre più 𝒇

8va
667
I
II
671
674
Ped.

677
28 71
Meno mosso
I
II
Meno mosso
682
687
cresc.

696

I

f

accel.

Ped.

II

701

I

706

I

rit.

8va

710

I

8va

29 72

Tempo I

II

Tempo I

8va

ff

8va
715
ff
Ped.
Ped.
Ped.
8va
I
II
(8va)
8va
720
8va
f
Ped.
Ped.
(8va)
726
8va
f
1
5
1
5
1
5
Ped.
f

730 8va

I

Ped.

II

734 (8va)

I

f

Ped.

II

30 73 8va

738

I

Ped.

II

(8va)
742
L
I
II
8vb
Ped.

746
8va
I
II
Ped.

750
I
II

755
I
II
Ped.
2
f
760
8va
f
Ped.
1
5
5
1
5
4
764
8va
1
Ped.

(8va)
768
I
II
4
Ped.
773
allargando
ff
1
❊
Ped.
allargando
f
778
a tempo
2
a tempo

783

allargando

ff

I

II

allargando

787

a tempo

8va

I

f

II

a tempo

f

793

I

2

II

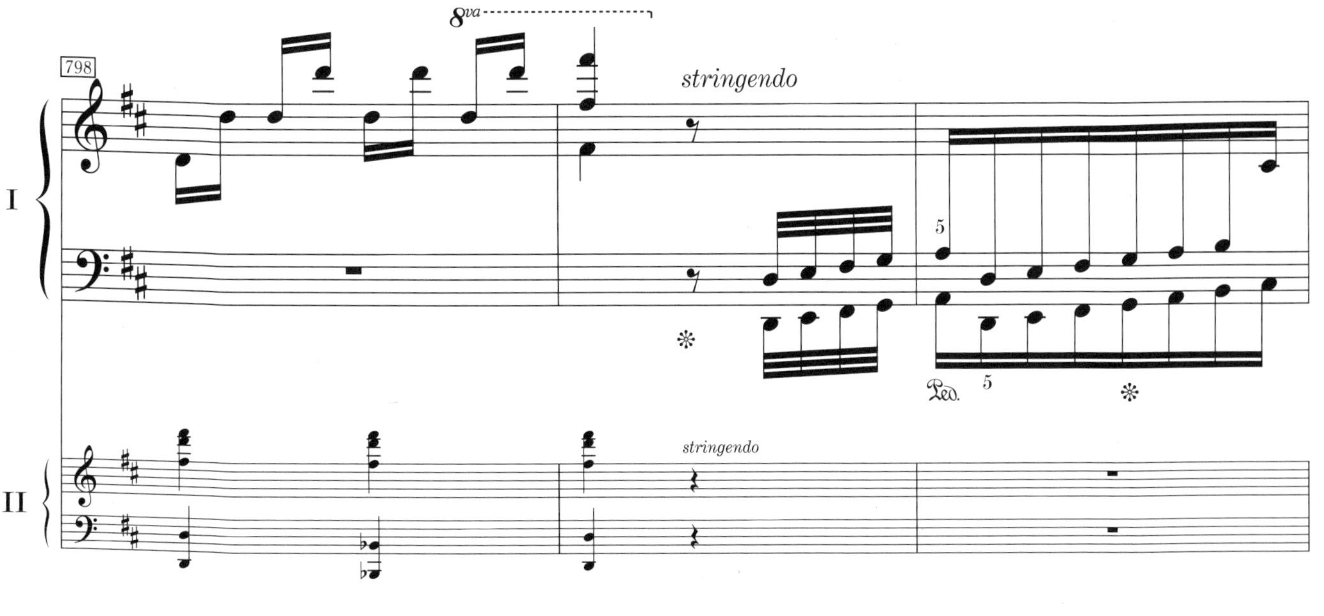
798
I
II
stringendo
8va
stringendo

801
I
II

805
I
II
8va
8va
trem.

MUSIC MINUS ONE
50 Executive Boulevard
Elmsford, New York 10523-1325
800-669-7464 (U.S.)/914-592-1188 (International)

www.musicminusone.com
e-mail: mmogroup@musicminusone.com

MMO 3079

Printed in Canada